Animal Tales

A treasury of animal adventures

templar publishing

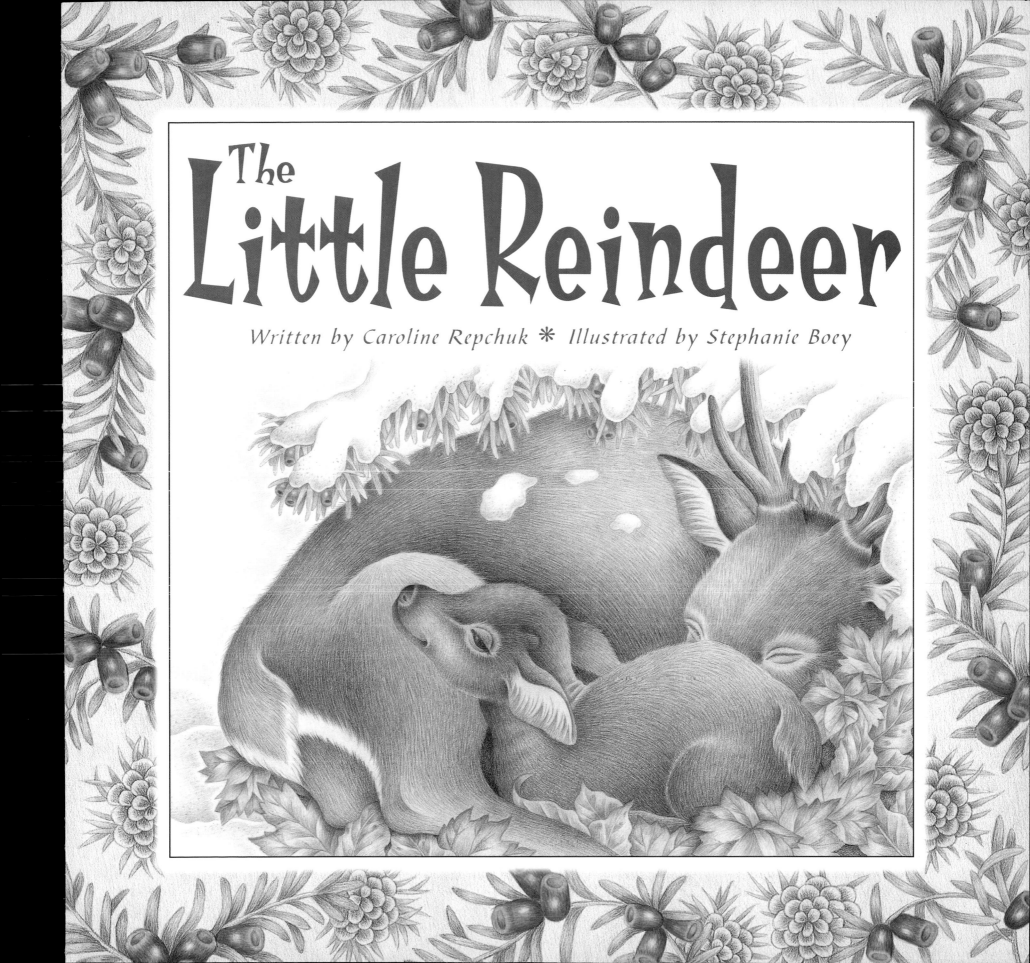

The Little Reindeer

Written by Caroline Repchuk ✳ Illustrated by Stephanie Boey

Little Reindeer gazed in wonder as fat snowflakes floated down and settled softly all around him. It was his first winter and, instead of the sweet grass of summer, the ground was covered in a snowy blanket.